My Second
Handwriting Activity Book

abcdefghijklm

My name is _michaellohn_

nopqrstuvwxyz

Letterland fairground

Write over the letters and add some more to finish the fairground scene.

PARENT POINTER

The letters **c**, **o**, **a**, **d**, **g** and **q** all start with the same circular handwriting movement. Point out the curved arrows. Explain that the dot is the starting point and then the arrow should be followed.

queue here

3

Putting up posters

Help the Letterlanders to fill up their posters by going over their letters and adding some more.

These letters are particularly useful for practising pencil control. With **f** and **t**, remind your child to write the horizontal cross bar from left to right and after the main letter stroke.

Impy's ink machine

Help Impy Ink and Uppy Umbrella by writing in their letter shapes.

Juggling jellies

Fill up these delicious jellies with Jumping Jim's letter and Yo-yo Man's letter.

Point out that the down stroke for the Yo-yo Man's letter and for Jumping Jim's letter goes through the line. Remind your child not to forget Jumping Jim's 'ball' (the dot) over his letter.

PARENT POINTER

7

Fun and games

Write these Letterlanders' letters on their play things for them.

Poor Peter's Pillow

PARENT POINTER

These letters - **h**, **b** and **p** - provide good practice in making a strong downward stroke, then a curve. It is important to notice where each letter meets the line.

8

Read all about it

These three Letterlanders have letters that all start the same way. Can you fill them in?

Nick's Noticeboard.

Robber Red

REWARD

Munching Mike's Magazine

Flying high

Fill in these letters up in the air! Except for Eddy Elephant's letter, they are all made with straight lines.

PARENT POINTER

Remind your child to begin Eddy Elephant's letter with a straight line before curving 'around his head'. All the straight letters provide practice in controlled short, sharp hand movements.

Capital letters

Help all the Letterlanders to fill in their capital letters. Remember to start at the top each time!

PARENT POINTER

The next four pages give your child plenty of practice in writing capital letters. Explain that capital letters are mostly used for starting important words like people's names, and for starting sentences.

j k l m n o p q

i j k l m n o p

h i j k l m n o

g h i j k l m n

f g h i j k l m

e f g h i j k

d e f g h i j

d e f g h i

Fairground Fun

The Letterlanders are having a lovely time on the rollercoaster. Help them by filling in the capital letters, as many times as you like!

N N N

O

P

Q

R

S S

First words

Now you can start writing whole words!
Write over the dotted words and then try writing
them by yourself.

abc

an acrobat

big bubbles

catch a cold

PARENT POINTER   The next eight pages give your child a chance to start writing words in
short, meaningful phrases. Encourage your child to say each word slowly
while writing it so he or she can hear the sounds each letter makes.

d e f

doll's dress

eleven eggs

fat frog

ghi

good game

happy horse

invite him in

18

j k l

jam jars

keep the kitten

long letter

19

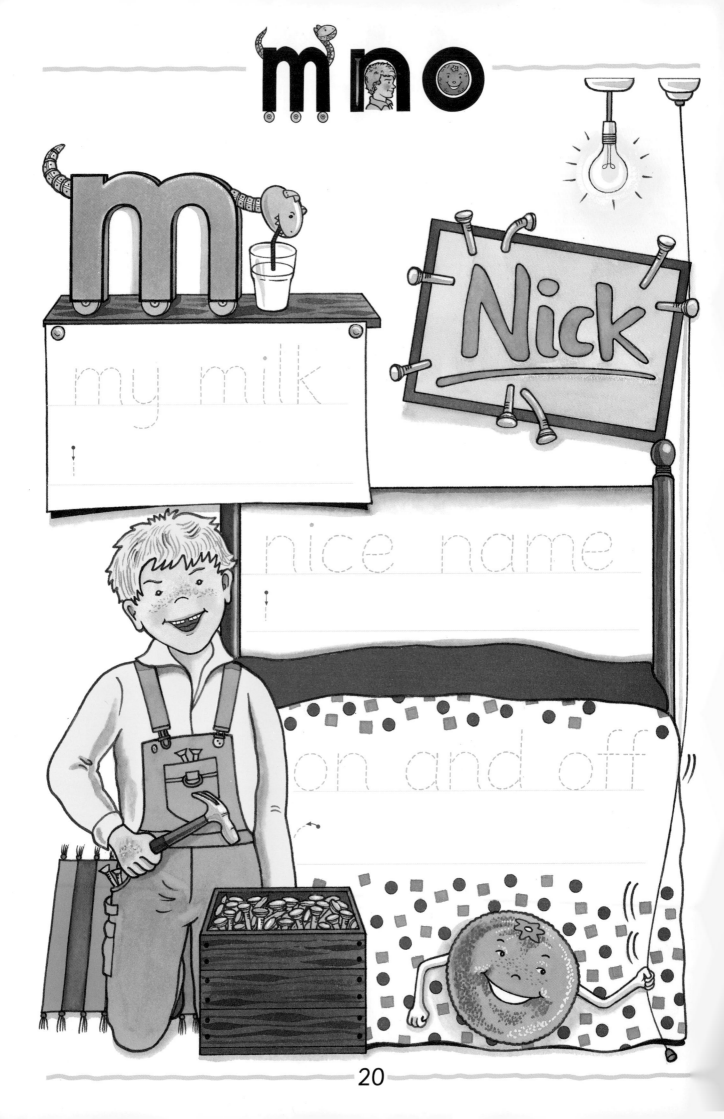

m n o

my milk

Nick

nice name

on and off

20

p q r

pink pig

quick quiz

red rug

stuv

soft snow

two trees

under the van

w x y z

windy weather

six yo-yos

lazy zebra

Days of the week

Write over these days of the week.

Monday

Tuesday

Wednesday

Thursday

Friday

Saturday

Sunday

PARENT POINTER

The words from page 16 onwards can be useful for practising reading as well as handwriting. Remember to be generous with praise, keep it fun and stop before your child gets tired.

24